Chicago. Originally manufactured in 1890 as the Munson, the name was changed to Chicago in 1898. Unusual features were the horizontal type-sleeve and the wide central ribbon. As on the Hammond, a hammer struck the paper against the type. It has a three-row keyboard with double shift.

OLD TYPEWRITERS

Duncan James

Shire Publications Ltd

CONTENTS

Printed in Great Britain by CIT Printing Services, Press Buildings, Merlins Bridge, Haverfordwest, Dyfed SA61 1XF.

British Library Cataloguing in Publication Data: James, Duncan. Old Typewriters. — (Shire Albums; No. 293). I. Title. II. Series. 652. 3. ISBN 0-7478-0193-2.

ACKNOWLEDGEMENTS
I am most grateful to Bernard Williams of Burton-on-Trent for allowing me to photograph some of the many fine typewriters in his superb collection. Other photographs are acknowledged as follows: Crown Copyright, Science Museum, London, pages 4, 5, 6 (bottom) and 22 (top left); IBM UK Ltd, page 29; and via Paul Lippman, page 28 (bottom).

Cover: *The Salter No. 10. Made by Salter & Company, scale makers of West Bromwich, this rugged machine had a three-row keyboard with porcelain key-tops and was sturdily built. The double shift was achieved by a to-and-fro movement of the carriage and a handle on the side allowed new ribbon to be wound on to the hidden spools. The first Salter (No. 5 with curved keyboard) came out in 1896 and the No. 10 in about 1910.*

Right: *The keyboard typewriter. It is helpful to understand that the design of the typewriter, especially in its earlier forms, is arranged in one of two basic ways. The first, and most familiar, is the keyboard typewriter, in which a range of keys is used for letter selection, either one character per key or, through the use of a shift mechanism, more than one character per key. The drawing shows the Imperial 50 of 1927.*

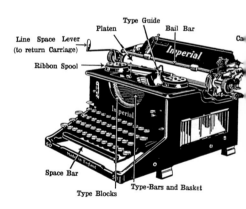

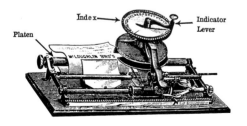

Left: *The index typewriter. The second form of typewriter is the index machine, in which the letter to be typed is selected by means of a pointer. Common features of index machines are that they are slow, of relatively simple design, and do not use type-bars. The illustration shows the rare McLoughlin of 1884, an American machine which originally sold for $10.*

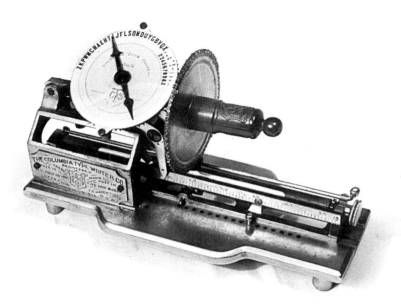

Columbia No. 2. Patented by Charles Spiro in America in 1885, the Columbia was a circular-index machine which included differential spacing but initially printed only in capitals. The No. 2 printed in both upper- and lower-case. Spiro also designed the Columbia Bar-Lock typewriter, which was made in England as the Royal Bar-Lock.

BEGINNINGS

In 1714 an English engineer, Henry Mill, outlined the concept of the typewriter when he registered a patent for 'an artificial machine … for impressing … letters … one after another, as in writing, whereby all writings…may be engrossed in paper or parchment, so neat and exact as not to be distinguished from print…'. Although nothing more is known of his design, it was the first of thousands of typewriter patents, which were especially numerous during the nineteenth century.

Some early attempts to make a typewriter sprang from the desire to help blind people read and write. This gave rise to simple index machines, such as the Hughes, which, although they were designed primarily to emboss the paper, were easily converted to printing by the use of carbon paper or an inked ribbon.

It was the wish to help the blind that prompted Pellegrino Turri, from Reggio in north Italy, to make the first working typewriter. Evidence for its existence rests securely on a series of poignant type-written letters produced between 1808 and 1810 by the blind Countess Carolina Fantoni, for whom the machine was specially constructed. Alas, this historic typewriter has not survived although the letters, the earliest examples of typing, have and they demonstrate that Turri's invention, which printed in capitals only, gave good line and letter spacing and used carbon paper to carry the image on to the paper.

Turri's typewriter was probably an index device, but that of another important Italian, Pietro Conti (1823), was a more sophisticated keyboard machine, called the

3

Tachigrafo, in which the type-bars struck upwards to print on the underside of the paper. This up-stroke typewriter, which was the first to make use of type-bars, inspired a fellow countryman, Giuseppe Ravizza, who, over a period of thirty years beginning in 1855, produced sixteen different models of his Cembalo Scrivano, also an up-stroke design, with a circular type-basket and, initially, a flat paten. The fact that the typing could not be viewed without lifting the paper was, to say the least, inconvenient. Unfortunately, none of Ravizza's ideas went into mass-production and eventually he was overtaken by developments in America.

There were many parallels between Ravizza's designs and those of the Austrian Peter Mitterhofer, who, beginning in 1864, constructed a series of crude wooden working models, but again none of them progressed to the stage of production.

Many pioneers were French, including Xavier Progin, who patented in 1833 a type-bar device called the Plume Typographique. This had type-bars which struck down on to the paper and therefore it had the distinction of being the first machine to offer visible writing, even though the visibility was limited by the machinery cluttered around the printing point. It was slow to operate and the pen was still a faster option.

In 1837 Gustave Bidet made two innovations: a typewriter that introduced the type-wheel and the first cylindrical platen. A few years later Pierre Foucault made the Raphigraphe, which was a radial-plunger machine for the blind. This was remarkable if only because Foucault himself was unable to see, yet he went on to develop his ideas in the Clavier Imprimeur (1849), which was even manufactured on a small scale.

Thus it was that in Europe, by the 1860s, many letters had been typed, usually with ponderous inaccuracy and at speeds slower than handwriting, on an impressive diversity of experimental machines. Also by this time almost every principal function of the typewriter had been invented by someone somewhere but, although a few inventors had managed to incorporate a number of these functions in a single machine, the truly practical, fast and accurate typewriter, with upper- and lower-case and fully visible script, had yet to appear. However, the time was ripe. The technology to mass-produce the machine was available and in the world of commerce the need for a speedy accurate means of letter writing was growing.

Hughes. This circular-index machine of 1850 was one of the first typewriters to be mass-produced, albeit in limited numbers. It printed embossed letters because it was made for the blind but it was later adapted for ordinary printing using carbon paper.

Hansen Writing Ball. The first model (1867) of this Danish radial thrust-action typewriter was mounted in a wooden case but the design was altered and improved before it was mass-produced by Jürgens Mekaniske Establissement. The machine had considerable success throughout Europe.

EARLY MASS-PRODUCTION

It was in Denmark that the first commercially successful typewriter, the Hansen Writing Ball, was produced. Its inventor, Pastor Malling Hansen, had wanted to help the blind and he reasoned that a ball-shaped arrangement of keys would allow touch-typing. From this he devised a radial type-plunger machine which underwent considerable development during its lifetime. Mass-production of this finely engineered curiosity began in 1870 and many were sold and used. But the design had no long-term future, because the action and the keyboard limited the speed. The wholly effective replacement for the pen was not found in Europe but was developed in the thriving cities of the industrial north-east of the United States.

The first American typewriter inventor of note was William Burt, who in 1829 produced his Typographer, a crude index device which, although cumbersome, had the merit of typing in both upper- and lower-case. He was followed by Charles Thurber, who in 1843 patented a type-plunger machine complete with carriage and platen.

Alfred Beach, editor of the *Scientific American*, made a typewriter in 1847 and followed it in 1856 with a more sophisticated machine using a combination of up-stroke and down-stroke type-bars which produced embossed letters as they converged upon the printing point from above and below the paper. It was intended for the blind and was limited to embossing on a narrow ribbon of paper although it seems also to have been adapted for printing using ribbon inking. The three-row keyboard was an advanced feature.

But it was the work of John Pratt of Alabama which had a seminal influence on the development of the typewriter in the USA. Pratt had, by 1863, produced a type-wheel machine which he found himself unable to patent because the United States was in the grip of its Civil War; so he took the idea across the Atlantic and secured an English patent in 1864. He then produced a plunger design (made in

5

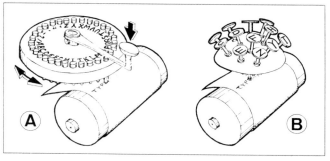

(A) The circular-index, type-plunger action as used on the Hughes. (B) The radial type-plunger action used on the Hansen.

Glasgow in 1865) but his Pterotype type-wheel machine of 1866, shown to the Society of Arts, London, was the design which received wide and significant publicity.

The full importance of Pratt's Pterotype is that through an article in the *Scientific American* (edited by Alfred Beach, the typewriter inventor) the machine came to the notice of Christopher Latham Sholes, an amateur inventor living in Milwaukee. At the time Sholes was working with Samuel Soule, a printer, making a page-numbering machine; but the detailed article concerning Pratt's machine, coupled with the encouragement of another colleague, Carlos Glidden, set him off in a new direction, inspired, however, more by Pratt's commitment to the idea of the typewriter than his actual design. Working together in a local machine shop, Sholes, Glidden and Soule produced an up-stroke typewriter for which a patent was filed in September 1867.

The prototype of this type-bar machine was crude and did not work at all well. It was also similar in many respects to the models made by Ravizza (1855) and Mitterhofer (1864), so it could hardly be regarded as an original invention. However, it was a start, but one which James Densmore, an entrepreneur who had invested in the project without seeing the machine, criticised heavily when he first set eyes on it. He pressed Sholes to make improvements, which resulted in a more compact patent of 1868. An attempt to manufacture this design failed and only fifteen machines were made. Densmore was undeterred. He was an unusual and forceful character, convinced that the machine had a future, so he insisted on further improvements and sank more money into the project.

In 1869 Sholes added a cylindrical

Pratt Pterotype. This was a good working type-wheel machine made in 1866. Although it was never mass-produced, it had a considerable influence on others, including Sholes and Hammond. The type-wheel was small, to allow it to rotate fast when a key was pressed. The key also released a small hammer which struck the paper from behind on to the type, a system later used in the Hammond because it gave even impressions. Inking was by means of a ribbon. Note the vertical paper carrier.

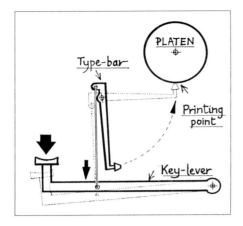

The up-stroke type-bar action. The simple up-stroke action was used by Mitterhofer and Ravizza and later on the Sholes & Glidden, Caligraph, Smith Premier and other typewriters between 1873 and 1900, usually with the type-bars arranged in a circle. The resultant basket-like structure came to be called the type-basket.

platen but with printing carried out round the roller and line spacing by means of carriage advance: exactly the reverse of the normal arrangement. But Densmore repeatedly forced Sholes to make more improvements. Even the great Thomas Edison saw the typewriter and suggested changes. Once more an attempt was made to manufacture it and although 25 were produced they were not good enough.

Densmore, desperate for money, tried (unsuccessfully, and for the second time) to sell the enterprise. A third effort was made to manufacture; it failed yet again.

By this time (1872) the project should have foundered. About thirty models had been made in the search for a satisfactory design and Densmore, who had put $31,000 into the project, had yet to see a return on his investment. Then George Washington Newton Yöst, a man who was to be important in the development of the typewriter, became involved. Yöst suggested asking the firm of E. Remington &

Sholes & Glidden. Historically, the most significant typewriter is the Sholes & Glidden of 1873. It had an up-stroke type-bar action, printed in capitals only and was the first machine with the universally adopted QWERTY keyboard. The lavish floral decoration shows the influence of the sewing-machine department in the Remington factory; indeed, the machine was at first supplied on a cast-iron stand with a treadle to operate the carriage return.

Sons of Ilion, New York, to manufacture the Sholes machine; it was a wise move.

Remington's fortunes had been built on the manufacture of small arms (especially lucrative during the American Civil War) but they were looking for alternative products. They had already diversified into sewing machines, so the typewriter was a reasonable, if speculative, undertaking. More importantly, Remington had experience in the mass-production of complex mechanisms and the proven ability to make them work.

Thus it was that on 1st March 1873 a manufacturing contract, negotiated by Yöst, was signed for a batch of one thousand machines, with an optimistic option for a further 24,000. This was all at very considerable cost, and the undaunted Densmore was forced to invest another $10,000 in the project.

The first typewriters that left the factory in 1874 were named the Sholes & Glidden. They were fine-looking machines with painted floral decoration which had

The Sholes & Glidden with platen/carriage assembly raised, showing the wide ribbon and the large-diameter, rubber-covered platen.

Caligraph No. 2. The Caligraph of 1881, the second American typewriter to go into mass-production, initially offered capitals only. Model No. 2, however, had a set of white keys for lower-case and black keys on each side for capitals; this was an arrangement known as a full keyboard.

more in common with the sewing machine and the boudoir than the commercial office. However, the mechanism within was promising. It had undergone improvements at the hands of two of Remington's experienced engineers and the typewriter did work, although it printed only capital letters. An additional drawback was that the printing was done on the hidden underside of the platen, which had to be lifted in order to inspect the work. Today, such an arrangement would be regarded as intolerable but 'non-visible' typewriters, of various makes, enjoyed considerable popularity over more than twenty years.

But the unique and lasting feature of the Sholes & Glidden was the QWERTYUIOP keyboard layout which is in worldwide use today in spite of being an illogical arrangement adopted merely in order to avoid adjacent typebars clashing. Ergonomically unsound, the QWERTY layout is an anachronism on the modern word-processor, but attempts to introduce a better system have, so far, failed.

REMINGTON AND ITS COMPETITORS

Initially, sales of the Sholes & Glidden typewriter were very poor — a mere hundred or so sold in the first year — and it aroused little interest at the Philadelphia Exhibition of 1876, where a remodelled and renamed machine, the Remington Improved Typewriter No.1, was displayed. Sales began to increase only with the introduction of the Model 2 of 1878, which incorporated the essential shift mechanism (invented in 1875 by Byron Brooks), allowing it to type in both upper- and lower-case. By this time some four thousand machines had been sold. With this growing commercial success, it was not long before competitors arrived on the scene.

One of the first was the Caligraph (1881), which was produced by G. W. N. Yöst in association with Franz X. Wagner. Both of these men had worked on the Remington and clearly drew on that experience. The Caligraph remained in production for 25 years.

Left: *Hall.* Thomas Hall, who abandoned an earlier and more sophisticated type-bar design *(patented in 1867), was successful with this anachronistic square-index typewriter, which was made in Salem, Massachusetts. It was placed on the market as late as 1881, in direct competition with a growing number of technically superior keyboard machines, and remained popular into the 1890s.*

Right: *Yöst No. 4.* Patented in 1889, the American Yöst could produce superbly aligned, high-quality print. The up-stroke grasshopper-action allowed the type to move from rest on an ink-pad and strike through a square type-guide on to the paper. The double keyboard had upper-case keys banked above the lower-case set. The No. 4 was produced in about 1894.

Yöst, however, moved on to develop an even more successful machine, the Yöst No. 1 (1889), which sidestepped the complication of a typewriter ribbon by using an unusual 'grasshopper' type-bar action which lifted the type from contact with an ink-pad and struck at the printing point through a special square type-guide. This produced well-aligned, high-quality print although the Yöst did have the disadvantage of a double keyboard. Another drawback was that, like both the Remington and the Caligraph, the Yöst was an up-stroke, non-visible design.

(A) Up-stroke type-bar, grasshopper-action as used on the early Yöst machines. (B) Front-stroke type-bar, grasshopper-action which was used on the later visible Yöst designs (after 1908). Both arrangements swung the type from the ink-pad to the paper in one smooth elegant movement.

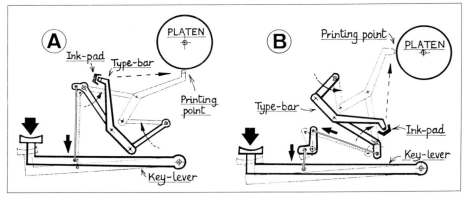

Hammond No. 2. Manufacture of the Hammond began in New York in 1881. Early machines were offered with a three-row Universal (QWERTY) keyboard or the curved two-row Ideal layout as shown on this No. 2 model of 1893. Three characters were obtainable from each key by means of a double shift. The Hammond's principal feature was its interchangeable type-sector (or shuttle). The paper, which was struck from behind on to the type, had to be wound down into the cylindrical wire basket below the platen before typing could begin.

A great machine of this period, named after its inventor (former Remington associate James B. Hammond), was the Hammond of 1881. It was a clever design which went some way towards offering visible typing. The Hammond was a radical development of the earlier Pratt Pterotype but instead of using Pratt's type-wheel it had a removable type-sector which allowed the typeface to be changed with ease. Later, this feature was the key to the Hammond's survival when an electric version, the VariTyper, was introduced in 1933 to become standard equipment for typesetting in the printing trade.

A typewriter related to the Hammond in its method of operation was the Crandall of 1881, devised by yet another former Remington man, Lucien Stephen Crandall. It featured a two-row keyboard with double shift in conjunction with a type-sleeve carrying six rows of characters. Only with the improvements built into later models, especially the Crandall No. 3 (1893), did the machine achieve success.

During the period from 1880 to 1900 there was a surge in the filing of typewriter-related patents as inventors struggled to find new principles by which the potentially lucrative typewriter might be made to work. As a result many clever and often extraordinary machines were launched on to the market by designers and manufacturers based in the north-east of the United States, all fiercely competing to make a superior machine whilst avoiding infringement of each other's patents. Many of the early typewriters' names testify to their origins in this enterprising corner of America: Arlington, Baltimore, Boston, Chicago, Cleveland, Dayton, Hartford, Manhattan, Niagara, Ohio, Pittsburgh, Philadelphia, Rochester and Woodstock.

Type-elements: (A) type-sector (shuttle); (B) type-wheel; (C) type-sleeve.

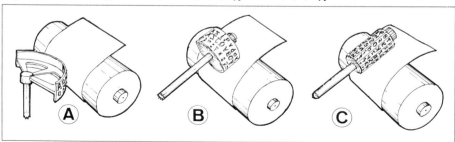

Above left: *Crandall New Model. The Crandall, the first production typewriter to use a type-sleeve (here partially hidden by the ribbon spool), was placed on the market in 1881. It was a highly decorative machine, inlaid with mother-of-pearl, and had a unique two-row keyboard layout which required a double shift. It was made in Groton, New York.*

Above right: *Smith Premier No. 4. The Smith Premier typewriter, which began manufacture in 1890 in Syracuse, New York, used a circular type-basket and up-stroke action, printing on the underside of the platen, which lifted to expose the line of type. The double keyboard avoided the need for a shift mechanism but made touch-typing impossible. The No. 4 is dated 1896.*

Below left: *Williams No. 1. The down-stroke, grasshopper-action type-bar of the Williams used direct inking of the type and offered full visibility. Because the type-bars struck from front and back it was necessary for the paper to feed between the holders below the platen. Production of the No. 1, with curved keyboard, started in 1891, the straight keyboard version appearing in 1892. The Williams Typewriter Company of Derby, Connecticut, closed in 1909.*

Below: *The down-stroke grasshopper-action type-bar as used on the Williams. The type hops from the ink-pad to the paper and back.*

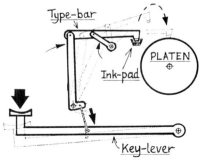

11

DESIGN IMPROVEMENTS

VISIBLE TYPING AT LAST

Before the end of the nineteenth century a host of famous typewriter companies were flourishing in the United States, including Oliver, Smith Premier, Williams, Yöst, Crandall, Bar-Lock, Blickensderfer and Hammond. All were vying with Remington for ascendancy in the market place.

A wide range of designs was on offer but, although many machines were relatively successful, no one had quite got the formula right — certainly not the Remington organisation, which, whilst introducing the improved Model 7 in 1897, failed to correct its one major drawback, that the typing on the underside of the platen was not readily visible to the typist.

This denial of the benefits of a type-writer offering visible typing is hard to understand, especially since such a machine, the Daugherty Visible of 1890, had arrived seven years earlier. This was a remarkable design in that it had an interchangeable type-basket — a feature which appeared later on the British-made Imperial machines. For some reason, perhaps because it was rather lightly built, the Daugherty was not the sweeping success it deserved to be.

But maybe the Daugherty had not gone unnoticed because in 1897 a famous front-stroke, fully visible typewriter, designed by Franz X. Wagner, was placed on the market. Wagner was the widely experienced inventor who had worked on Yöst's Caligraph and before that on the Sholes & Glidden, and his new machine, pat-

Left: *Remington No. 5. The typewriter is shown with its platen raised to expose the wide ribbon (1¼ inches, 32 mm) which these early machines used. Like its predecessor, the Sholes & Glidden, it had wooden key-levers and also retained the up-stroke type-bar action. It is estimated that about fifteen thousand examples of this model of 1887 were manufactured.*

Right: *Daugherty Visible. This was the first front-stroke production typewriter which offered fully visible typing. It was also notable for having a removable keyboard/type-bar unit. Produced in 1890, it was renamed the Pittsburg Visible in 1898.*

Left: *Underwood No. 5. The Underwood No. 5 (1901), which had a superior mechanism to the superficially similar No. 1 of 1896, set the standard for office typewriters. It had a light touch, offered fully visible typing and was fitted with an integral tabulator. It was also a fine piece of engineering which remained in production, with few changes, for thirty years.*

Right: *Sholes Visible. Designed by the famous C. L. Sholes and patented in 1891, this typewriter had a unique but slow type-bar action. Sholes's son Louis organised the production, which began in 1902, but the machine was not very successful. It was made by the Meiselbach Typewriter Company of Wisconsin.*

ented in 1893, was the Underwood No. 1. It was financed by John T. Underwood, who had for some years been supplying carbon paper and typewriter ribbon to Remington. The decision by Remington to begin manufacturing their own ribbon had angered Underwood and prompted his entry into typewriter manufacture. He was lucky because Wagner's design was a winner. The No. 1 was quickly improved and the No. 5, launched in 1901, sold by the million throughout the world. The machine was of front-stroke design with a light touch to the keyboard and an integral tabulator; it remained almost unchanged for over thirty years and set the pattern for office typewriter design for many years to come.

(A) Front-stroke type-bar action (Daugherty Visible, Underwood 5). (B) Oblique front-stroke type-bar action (Ideal).

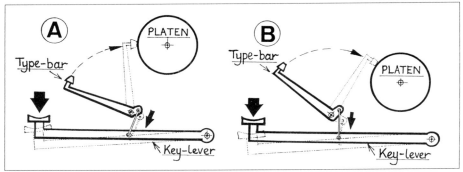

Remington No. 10. This design of 1908 was the first Remington which offered visible writing. Some features of the earlier machines were retained, such as the positioning of the ribbon spools and especially the substantial bearings at the type-bar pivots, which avoided the need for a type-guide at the printing point. The No. 10 had a lighter touch than its predecessors.

UNIVERSAL FOUR-ROW KEYBOARD (QWERTY)

DOUBLE KEYBOARD (QWERTY)

UNIVERSAL THREE-ROW KEYBOARD (QWERTY)

IDEAL KEYBOARD (DHIATENSOR)

Ten years after the introduction of the Underwood, Remington belatedly produced a comparable machine, also with a tabulator and offering visible typing. This was the Remington No. 10 of 1908.

KEYBOARDS

An integral part of striving to manufacture the best typewriter was the challenge of finding the best keyboard. The QWERTY (Universal) four-row keyboard, offering upper-case by means of a single shift, had become accepted at an early stage through the Sholes & Glidden/ Remington lineage.

But other layouts were promoted, the most important being the double keyboard, which avoided the complication of a shift mechanism but only by using twice the number of keys and type-bars. The early Smith Premiers, Yösts, Bar-Lock and others had the double keyboard with a QWERTY layout for lower-case and above it a duplicate set of keys for capi-

Four of the more common keyboard arrangements found on early typewriters. Many subtle variations of these exist, especially for foreign languages. The four-row Universal (QWERTY) layout of the 1870s is still in daily use throughout the world on the keyboards of the most advanced computers.

tals. It was an arrangement which lasted for some decades but declined in popularity as it was realised that high-speed typing was possible only by touch-typing. This technique, in which the operator types without looking at the keyboard, was developed after 1880 and proved to be impossible on the cumbersome double-keyboard machines.

A compressed version of the QWERTY keyboard was the three-row layout with double shift, offering three characters per key — an arrangement which was widely adopted, especially for portable machines, because it economised on weight and space by reducing the number of type-bars and key-levers.

Even greater economy was achieved on the Helios, with its two-row keyboard and triple shift; it had just 21 keys to give 84 characters but found little favour.

The keyboard which offered the most serious challenge to the Universal QWERTY layout was the Ideal keyboard, a three-row arrangement in which the letters in the bottom row were DHIATENSOR. This Ideal keyboard (not to be confused with the Ideal typewriter) used a double shift and was available on the Blickensderfer and Hammond machines for many years.

Left, top: *Smith Premier No. 10b. In 1908, when Remington brought out the No. 10, Smith Premier modernised their up-stroke design to give front-stroke visible typing, but they must have had a strong following for the double keyboard, since they left that feature unchanged. The 'b' version of the Model 10 incorporated a ten-key tabulator. Production ceased possibly as late as 1921.*

Left, centre: *Royal No. 6. The first model of the Royal, introduced in 1905, was an advanced typewriter with a low profile, offering fully visible typing. The improved No. 5 of 1911, had a two-colour ribbon and a tabulator. The No. 6 (1912), shown here, was a long-carriage version of the No. 5.*

Left, bottom: *Helios. The compact Helios was made in Germany between 1908 and 1914. Its two-row keyboard had a triple shift and the type was carried in four tiers around a type-wheel.*

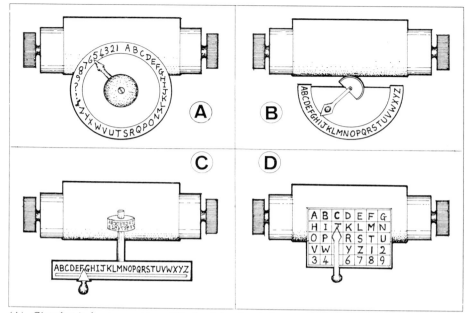

(A) Circular-index typewriter. (B) Semicircular-index typewriter. (C) Linear-index typewriter. (D) Square- or rectangular-index typewriter.

INDEX TYPEWRITERS

In parallel with developments in keyboard typewriters of this period many forms of index machine were made. In these the type was brought to the printing point either by rotating a circular index wheel or dial (Velograph, 1886; Columbia, 1886); or by swinging a lever along a curved index scale (Kosmopolit, 1888); or by sliding a linear index (Hammonia, 1884; Odell, 1889; Merritt, 1890); or even by using a pointer for selection (Mignon,

Velograph. Patented in 1886 and manufactured in Geneva, the large circular-index Velograph was the first Swiss typewriter. This is the second model of 1887. Inking was by ribbon.

Left: *Mignon No. 4. This square-index machine, invented in 1903, was manufactured by AEG, Berlin, and others until, by the late 1930s, some 350,000 had been produced. Moving the pointer selected the required character. One advantage of this machine was the ease with which the type and the index plate could be changed. The major disadvantage was the limited speed of the typing, although the manufacturers claimed 250 to 350 characters per minute!*

Right: *Merritt. This small linear-index double shift typewriter used a row of printer's type, sliding in a groove beneath the platen. When the selector lever was pressed a piece of type was lifted up to strike the underside of the platen, which could be raised to view the typing. A roller was used to ink the type. Manufactured in Springfield, Massachusetts, 1892, and later in New York.*

1904). Such designs were generally produced for home rather than office use since they were cheaper (some very cheap) and slower (some impossibly slow). However, in the years before the widespread use of the portable typewriter it is clear that index devices would have been a first introduction to typing for many people.

The index principle was also used widely on tinplate toy typewriters of all periods. Typical of these was the Simplex, which had a circular index with rubber type fixed around the edge. Many different models were made in the United States between about 1895 and 1950. Another American make was the Marx dial (c.1923-40). Similar in operation to the Simplex, it featured a printed dummy keyboard. Toy machines were usually supplied in printed cardboard boxes, which often help in dating them.

Junior. A toy index typewriter with inking by roller. The tinplate body carries a dummy keyboard. German, c.1920/30.

Top left: *Lambert. A form of circular-index typewriter (it might also be classified as a keyboard machine), which had an unusual radial-plunger action. The index disc did not revolve: instead it tilted when a key was pressed, pushing the selected character to the printing point. Patented between 1884 and 1896, the Lambert was manufactured in New York and later (1900-4) in England by The Gramophone and Typewriter Company. Versions were also made in France and Germany.*

Top right: *Hammonia. This simple linear-index typewriter was invented by Andrew Hansen in London, patented in 1882 and made by the sewing-machine manufacturers Guhl & Harbeck in Germany.*

Bottom left: *American Visible. This simple rectangular index typewriter used a linear strip of rubber type which was inked using a pad. The metal cradle held the operator's finger tip.*

Bottom right: *Odell No. 4. A robust linear-index typewriter, patented in 1889. The No. 4 of 1904 was made in Chicago.*

Ideal. The superb Ideal typewriter was an oblique front-stroke machine patented by E. E. Barney, Groton, USA, in 1897. It was manufactured by Seidal & Naumann, Germany.

THE TYPEWRITER IN GERMANY AND BRITAIN

Whilst it could not be said that the typewriter was invented in the USA, it is certain that between the Sholes & Glidden of 1873 and the Underwood No. 1 of 1897 it grew from infancy to manhood. These developments did not go unnoticed and as the American machines were sold into Europe mass-production of typewriters began in other countries.

Since Germany already had strong links with industrial America (cities like Milwaukee, where the Sholes & Glidden was created, had many German immigrants), it is no surprise to find a feedback of ideas. The superb Ideal typewriter, for example, was made by the sewing-machine manufacturers Seidal & Naumann AG in Dresden to an 1897 patent by the American E. E. Barney.

A more significant link is the way in which the Adlerwerke cycle-manufacturing company of Frankfurt laid the foundations of the Adler typewriter company following its licensed production, beginning in 1898, of W. P. Kidder's thrust-action Empire, which subsequently was developed into both office and portable versions.

Not all German designs were imported, however; machines like the robust Kosmopolit (1888) and the extraordinary Kanzler of 1903 were indigenous inventions.

English inventors also produced some independent thinking on the subject of the typewriter. The idea of the typewriter ribbon, for instance, was patented in 1841 by Alexander Bain in the course of making a printer for use with the electric telegraph.

Another pioneering design became one of the earliest mass-produced typewriters in the world: a circular-index device by G. A. Hughes, governor at Manchester Blind Asylum. His machine, originally intended for the blind, embossed the paper but it was converted to produce conventional typing by the use of carbon paper.

A number of fine British typewriters were introduced in the 1890s, but none of them was manufactured for longer than about ten years.

Left: *Empire No. 2. This very successful radial thrust-action typewriter, manufactured in Canada, was patented by Wellington Parker Kidder in 1892. A similar design, the Wellington, was also made in New York from 1895 whilst Adler in Germany produced a succession of different models based on the thrust-action principle. The Empire No. 2 dates from 1909.*

Right: *Kosmopolit. Following production of the Hammonia, the German firm of Guhl & Harbeck made the sturdy Kosmopolit. Invented in 1888, it was a semicircular-index machine, with a curved type-sector, which was only slightly more sophisticated than their earlier typewriter*

Left: *Kanzler No. 3. An unusual German thrust-action typewriter with eight characters on each of only eleven type-bars. It was manufactured by Kanzler Schreibmaschinen A G between about 1903 and 1912.*

One of the more improbable British designs was the fascinating grasshopper-action Maskelyne (1889/90), the invention of the famous illusionist John Nevil Maskelyne (1839-1917). The machine even incorporated differential spacing, as did the Waverley of 1889. This was a down-stroke machine with four-row keyboard and shift, although there were separate type-bars for each character.

The so-called English typewriter of 1890 had type-bars that struck down from the front. This obscured the typist's view

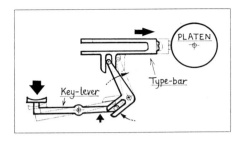

The thrust-action type-bar as used in the Wellington, Empire and Adler.

Left: *Bing No. 1. Made in 1925 by Bingwerke A G, a German company famous for its tinplate toys, this typewriter used thin steel pressings to achieve a lightweight oblique front-stroke machine. The pad inking arrangement was modified to inking by ribbon in the No. 2 model of 1927.*

Below: *Bee. This linear-index, type-wheel design was made in Germany in 1934. The Bakelite housing is an unusual feature which helped to keep the weight down to 4 pounds (1.8 kg). It was also made with the name Carissima.*

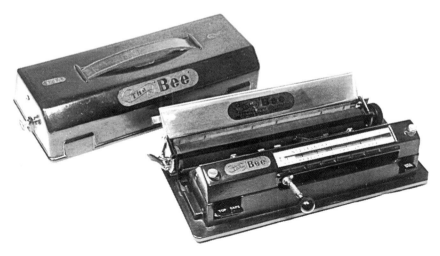

Above left: *Maskelyne. Using a grasshopper-action similar to the Williams, the English Maskelyne of 1889 incorporated differential spacing. A second model, the Maskelyne Victoria, was produced in 1897. Inking was by pad.*

Above right: *Waverley. The down-stroke Waverley, manufactured in England in 1895, used a shift mechanism which engaged a separate upper-case set of type-bars rather than shifting the platen or type-basket. The curved bars in front of the platen were for holding the paper as it fed through the rollers. The machine included differential spacing and inking by ribbon.*

Below left: *North's. The curiously named North's, a down-stroke single-shift machine, was a successor to the English typewriter. It was unusual in that the open-ended carriage allowed very wide paper, such as legal documents, to be inserted. It was manufactured by North's Typewriter Manufacturing Company, London, 1892.*

Below right: *Gardner. Made in Manchester between 1893 and 1895, the Gardner failed in the market place because of its impossible keyboard which required simultaneous depression of up to three keys in various combinations. The small number of keys (fourteen) was an attempt to simplify the machine. Type-sleeve with inking by roller.*

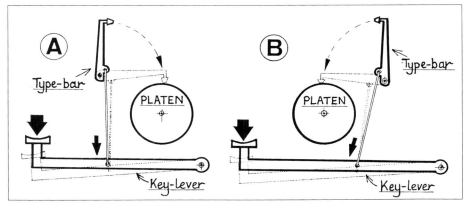

Down-stroke type-bar actions: (A) front; (B) rear. The down-stroke action from the front resulted in a phalanx of type-bars which obscured the typist's view of the typing, as on the Royal Bar-Lock, Imperial B and Salter No. 10. This visibility problem was solved by striking down from the back of the machine although this created difficulties with what to do with the paper (North's, Waverley).

of the typing and subsequently the same factory produced a more successful design (the North's) in which the bars struck down from the back in a similar manner to the Waverley.

An early British attempt at making a type-sleeve machine was the Gardner, pro-duced in Manchester in 1893. It was a failure because, in trying to reduce the number of parts, the inventor had devised an extraordinary keyboard which was ab-surdly difficult to use.

A more conventional typewriter was the fine-looking Salter, made by the famous

Royal Bar-Lock No. 14. The Bar-Lock design, with its double key-board, was patented in the United States in 1889 by Charles Spiro and manufactured by the Colum-bia Typewriter Company, New York. It was the first machine to use an automatic ribbon-revers-ing mechanism. Models 1, 2 and 3 had fancy cast-iron type-bar shields whilst those for models 4 to 7 were heavily embellished de-signs with a copper finish. The machine illustrated (dated 1910) has a more modest pressed-steel type-bar shield and was sold by the Bar-Lock Typewriter Company of Nottingham. The name 'Bar-Lock' referred to the semicircle of between eleven and fifteen pins or bars at the printing point, which acted as alignment guides for the type-bars. The machine had no connection with the Royal Type-writer Company.

Left: *Bar-Lock No. 16. This front-stroke machine was introduced in 1921 to replace the Royal Bar-Lock. It was of robust construction with an interchangeable carriage. The design remained almost unchanged for over thirty years.*

Right: *Oliver No. 11. The Oliver was a very successful and robust typewriter with a unique lateral down-stroke action. Launched in 1894, the distinctive design remained basically the same through a succession of fifteen models over a fifty-year period of production. Manufacture of the Oliver closed in America in 1928 but continued in England until as late as 1947. The No. 11 dates from 1922.*

West Bromwich firm better known for manufacturing scales. Patented in 1892, the No. 5, with a curved keyboard, was the first model of this down-stroke design.

The influence of the United States can be traced clearly in the history of a number of British typewriter manufacturers. The Bar-Lock Typewriter Company in Nottingham, for example, started as a sales

The lateral down-stroke type-bar action as used on the Oliver.

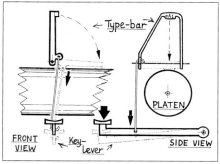

agency for the Columbia Bar-Lock typewriter but when the American company ceased trading in 1914 the Nottingham factory purchased the tools and machinery and in 1921 launched its own front-stroke, the Bar-Lock No. 16. The business survived until 1958, when the problems associated with the introduction of a radically new design of typewriter, the Byron of 1957, forced the factory to close. The assets were purchased by the Oliver Typewriter Company of Croydon, which itself had started life in 1928 when it bought up the production facilities of the American Oliver Company.

The Oliver typewriter, a lateral down-stroke machine first manufactured in 1894, was designed by the Reverend Thomas Oliver. Its unusual shape and robust construction have ensured that many survive in working order. Incredibly, production of this relic ended, in England, as late as 1947.

The greatest of the British typewriter manufacturers, the Imperial Typewriter Company, also had American origins through Hidalgo Moya, its founder. Moya, an American who had worked in the New York Hammond factory, arrived in Leicester in 1902 with a type-sleeve machine of his own design. He succeeded in manufacturing a Model No. 1 and in 1905 Model 2, but real success came only when his company was re-financed and began production of the front-stroke type-bar Imperials A, B and later the D model. The larger Model 50 (1927), with its interchangeable keyboard, remained in production for many years.

Right: *Moya No. 1. Manufactured in 1903 in Leicester, this was the first typewriter from what later became the Imperial Typewriter Company. The machine used a type-sleeve, with inking by ribbon from two stacked spools. The Model 2 of 1905 had slightly improved visibility, with the ribbon spools placed on each side of the chassis. Production ceased in 1908.*

Left: *Imperial Model B. The first completely successful Imperials were the similar A and B models of 1908 and 1915 respectively. This down-stroke semi-portable design had a three-row curved keyboard with double shift. The keyboard/type-bar assembly was interchangeable. The model D of 1921 had a straight keyboard.*

Right: *Imperial Model 50. Entering the market in 1927 the Model 50 was, for a standard office typewriter, a late arrival. It was, however, very successful and production continued until 1955. The carriage, platen and key/type-bar assembly were all easily exchangeable.*

Above left: *Remington Noiseless Portable. Remington introduced their noiseless portable in about 1930. The type-bar linkage had an overthrow weight to slow down the speed of impact of the type. The model shown here was for the French market.*

Above right: *Imperial Good Companion No. 1. Introduced in 1932, this very successful design was a development of the German Torpedo-Werke Mead portable. The friendly name 'Good Companion' was derived from the title of a novel by J. B. Priestley. Production of the model No. 7 ended in 1966.*

Left: *Blickensderfer No. 7. A very lightweight American type-wheel design starting with the No. 5 of 1893, of which the subsequent models were all variations. The No. 7 came out in 1897. The three-row keyboard was offered as QWERTY (Universal) or DHIATENSOR (Ideal) layouts, and type-wheels were available for many languages and styles.*

Below left: *Standard Folding. On this early portable of 1907 the carriage folded forward over the keyboard. To reduce weight, the chassis was made from aluminium. Invented by Frank Rose in the USA, the design evolved to become the Corona Folding.*

Below right: *Corona No. 3 Folding Portable. Closely based on the Standard Folding, the Corona of 1912 was very successful and continued in production until 1941, by which time about 700,000 had been made.*

Underwood Portables No. 3 and No. 4. The diminutive No. 3 portable of 1919 had a production life of ten years. It was replaced by the four-row keyboard portable of 1926.

FURTHER DEVELOPMENTS

THE NOISELESS TYPEWRITER

When it was realised that the unpleasant clatter in the office was due to the percussive effect of the type on the paper, W. P. Kidder, designer of the thrust-action Empire, and C. C. Colby evolved a design, patented in 1896, which reduced the speed of the impact of the type. This was achieved using an overthrow weight and a complex series of linkages on each typebar which slowed the type down as it approached the platen and pressed it firmly on to the paper to print the character. The machine was manufactured in America in 1912 by the Noiseless Typewriter Company.

Curiously, the lack of a satisfying click when the type meets the paper is disconcerting and may have been the reason for the limited adoption of what seems to be a good idea. However, Remington purchased the company in 1924 and produced both office and portable versions, as did the Underwood factory. The noiseless typewriter faded from production in about 1950.

THE PORTABLE TYPEWRITER

Although the standard form of front-stroke office typewriter, the Underwood No. 1, had appeared in 1897, it took longer for the definitive design of portable typewriter to arrive. Many index designs could, because of their small size, qualify as portables but their lack of speed meant that they were not a serious challenge to keyboard typewriters.

Undoubtedly the first successful portable was the Blickensderfer, a simple, light and ingenious type-wheel design, which had been produced for the businessman on the move. The ability to change the typeface (type-wheels covering many languages and print-styles were available) was one reason for its popularity. The growth of the company dates from 1893 with the introduction of the No. 5, which was developed into a range of variations including the Blick Featherweight (1896), which incorporated aluminium, a newly available metal. An improved version, the Model 7, was produced in 1897.

But there were competitors, such as the Corona Folding Portable. This delicate machine was a light and compact typebar design, with ribbon inking, whose principal feature was a hinged carriage which folded forward over the three-row keyboard to allow the typewriter to fit into a small plywood case. It was de-

signed by Frank Rose and his son and marketed in 1907 by the Rose Typewriter Company, which became the Standard Typewriter Company in 1909, then finally in 1914 the Corona Typewriter Company. It remained in production as late as 1941 in spite of the introduction of the non-folding, conventional four-row keyboard Corona Four in 1924.

Early in its history Frank Rose's typewriter inspired other folding designs: one, the Bijou or Erika, was made in Germany by Seidal & Naumann. Even smaller than the Corona Folding was the Underwood three-row portable of 1919, which was followed in 1926 by a four-row version.

The typewriter company which was first to make a four-row portable was Remington, with the 'collapsible bar' portable of 1920. This machine achieved a low profile of only 3 inches (75 mm) because the type-bars folded down when not in use. But such a compact typewriter was not necessarily what the public wanted and subsequent models steadily increased in size; by 1950 the Remington portable had doubled in size.

Soon all the big companies had four-bank portables: Royal in 1926; Erika No. 5 in 1927; Oliver, 1930; Imperial, Olivetti

Blickensderfer Electric. The electric Blick was a motorised version of the manual Blickensderfer. The first model appeared in 1902, the second in about 1913. With its type-wheel and electric action, it foreshadowed the IBM 'golf-ball' typewriter of 1961.

Electromatic. As ancestor to the IBM series of electric type-writers, the Electromatic of 1924 has an important place in typewriter history. It made use of the powered roller system (later widely adopted) for driving both the type-bars and carriage.

and Adler, 1932; Olympia, 1933; and Torpedo with the Blue Bird portable in 1935.

Because they were intended for home use, many portables were produced in colour — red, green and blue were favourites — although black remained the usual finish. During and after the Second World War black, grey and green crackle paint finishes were common although on an office machine crackle paint often indicates that the typewriter has been stripped down and reconditioned.

THE ELECTRIC TYPEWRITER

The final phase in the development of the typewriter during the twentieth century was the manufacture of a satisfactory electric machine. This became a desirable goal because large machines with long carriages made considerable physical demands on the typist. It was also realised that an electric typewriter could offer a light keyboard touch, fast type-bar action and give an even print impression.

The Hansen Writing Ball was one of the first typewriters to use electricity, but only to power an electromagnetic escapement release.

The first successful electric typewriter was the now rare Blickensderfer Electric, a motorised version of the famous Blick type-wheel machine. The first model, introduced in 1902, was remarkable in that both the printing and carriage movements were controlled from the keyboard.

But it was ahead of its time and did not sell in any quantity. This may have been partly because few offices at the time had electric power during the day — its use being limited to night-time lighting.

Other attempts were made. The German Mercedes Electra (1921) incorporated a powered roller from which the drive to carriage and type-bars was taken; this system was widely used in later machines, including the Woodstock Electrite of 1925. The Remington electric of 1925, however, was semi-electric and only 2500 were made.

Perhaps the first manufacturer to make a commercial success of the electric typewriter was IBM, which had bought up the Electromatic of 1924, and from this design developed a new machine which was launched in 1935. IBM achieved an even greater success with the creation of the Selectric 'golf-ball' typewriter of 1961, which abolished the moving carriage. Instead of the paper travelling past the printing point, the type-element moved across the paper.

So, in a little over a century the mechanical typewriter has grown up and grown old. Now, with the advent of the word-processor, it is seriously outclassed and almost extinct. But the typewriter will certainly live on as an example of engineering skill and inventive cunning with few parallels in the world of creative technology.

Left: *Edison Mimeograph typewriter. Thomas Edison may have had little to do with the design of this solid and relatively primitive circular-index machine. The connection with the great inventor is that it was made for cutting wax stencils which could then be used on the Edison Mimeograph duplicator. The type-plunger action struck upwards on the underside of the platen, the plungers falling back by force of gravity. Characters were selected by rotating the disc at the base of the machine. It was manufactured in Chicago in about 1894, by A. B. Dick & Company, who also made the duplicators.*

Right: *Victor. This semicircular-index typewriter, which used a vertical type-disc with rubber type, is one of the forerunners of the modern daisy-wheel printer. Made in Boston, USA, in 1894.*

Left: *Virotyp. This small French circular-index typewriter, dating from 1914, was originally made to be strapped to the wrist and used on horseback in wartime. The illustration shows a slightly later desk-top version.*

COLLECTING TYPEWRITERS

It is desirable that a typewriter should work, if only for the pleasure of using a machine that may be a hundred years old. However, the appearance is vital since rust, plated parts that are peeling and faded or damaged paintwork can ruin an attractive machine. Never attempt to repaint an old machine, for the result is seldom good.

A major difficulty, linked to poor storage conditions, is that rubber components deteriorate. Thus the platen surface can harden, crack and disintegrate, whilst the rubber feet may soften and decay to form a sticky mess.

Many early machines were supplied in bentwood or steel cases, and these increase their chances of survival. Portables, which were made with cases, usually rexine-covered plywood, have a good survival rate. Plywood, however, must be kept dry and checked regularly for woodworm (furniture beetle).

Old machinery may suffer from too much oil, which oxidises and, with the accumulation of dust, clogs the mechanism. Thin oil from a pressurised spraycan is helpful in freeing up the works.

Serial numbers are important in dating typewriters but, although almost all machines are numbered, locating them can be a challenge. The most likely place is on the typewriter chassis beneath the right-hand end of the carriage.

Left: The typewriter brought women into the commercial world as never before and introduced temptation into the office as never before. Many postcards were issued showing coy type-writers (typists) with their typewriters (here an early Remington). Possibly typewriter manufacturers were attempting to achieve extra sales by hinting at the other opportunities which the machine could open up.

Right: A type-writer, as the first typists were called, is shown operating a Rem-Sho typewriter of 1896, complete with copy holder. The Rem-Sho was placed on the market by F. R. Remington and Zalmon G. Sholes, the son of C. L. Sholes. The body of the typewriter, with its columns and decoration, was designed by an architect, Charles B. Atwood. In a world of black machines, the Rem-Sho had an unusual matt bronze finish.

FURTHER READING

Adler, Michael H. *The Writing Machine, a History of the Typewriter.* George Allen & Unwin, London, 1973.

Beeching, Wilfred A. *Century of the Typewriter.* William Heinemann, London, 1974.

Bliven, Bruce, Jr. *The Wonderful Writing Machine.* Random House, New York, 1954.

Lippman, Paul. *American Typewriters, A Collector's Encyclopedia.* Original & Copy, 1216 Garden Street, Hoboken, New Jersey 07030, USA, 1992.

Richards, G. Tilghman. *The History and Development of Typewriters.* Science Museum, HMSO, London, 1964.

PLACES TO VISIT

Museum displays may be altered and readers are advised to telephone before visiting to check that relevant items are on show, as well as to find out the opening times.

Birmingham Museum of Science and Industry, Newhall Street, Birmingham, West Midlands B3 1RZ. Telephone: 021-236 1022. Important collection of fifty typewriters, six on display.

John George Joicey Museum, City Road, Newcastle upon Tyne, Tyne and Wear NE1 2AS. Telephone: 091-232 4562. Twenty-five typewriters in collection, a few on display.

Milton Keynes Museum of Industry and Rural Life, Stacey Hill Farm, Southern Way, Wolverton, Milton Keynes, Buckinghamshire MK12 5EJ. Telephone: 0908 319148. Thirty typewriters in collection, seven on display.

Nottingham Industrial Museum, Courtyard Buildings, Wollaton Park, Nottingham NG8 2AE. Telephone: 0602 284602. Thirty typewriters in collection, none on display.

Royal Museum of Scotland, Chambers Street, Edinburgh EH1 1JF. Telephone: 031-225 7534. Important collection of one hundred typewriters, a few on display.

Science Museum, Exhibition Road, South Kensington, London SW7 2DD. Telephone: 071-938 8000. Very important collection of one hundred typewriters, a few on display.

Snibston Discovery Park, Former Snibston Mine, Ashby Road, Coalville, Leicestershire LE6 2LN. Telephone: 0530 813301. Very important collection of two hundred typewriters, twelve on display.

Stockport Museum, Vernon Park, Turncroft Lane, Stockport, Cheshire SK1 4AR. Telephone: 061-474 4460. Thirty typewriters in collection, a few on display.

Woolstaplers Hall Museum, High Street, Chipping Campden, Gloucestershire GL55 6HB. Telephone: 0386 840289. Important collection of thirty typewriters, all on display.